Dear Book-Buyer,

Do you know what a *diary* really is?

It's a book filled with letters—
letters that you write to yourself!

We've divided this diary into two parts.
Part One has special pages with ideas to
help you get started. Part Two has special
pages for the twelve months of the year.
We started in January, but you may skip
ahead to whichever month it is when you start
your journal.

Happy Writing!   Sincerely,

The People at
Willowisp Press

P.S.: Nobody, but NOBODY, gets to read what you write
in your diary—unless you say so!!

Published by Willowisp Press, Inc.
401 E. Wilson Bridge Road, Worthington, Ohio 43085

Printed in the United States of America

10 9 8 7 6 5 4 3

ISBN 0-87406-223-3

MY VERY OWN DIARY

This book was written by *Paula Brott* .

It was started on _____, 1991 _____, 19 91 .
day of the week   month of the year and   year
                          day of the month

It was finished on _____, _____, 19 _____ .
day of the week   month of the year and   year
                          day of the month

PART ONE STARTS ON THE NEXT PAGE ↓

_____, 19____

Dear Diary,

Well, you're probably wondering who I am,
so I will introduce myself.

My full name is _Paula Brill_,

and my nickname is _Paluskiy_.

I was born on _July 12 / 1984_,

in _montreal_.

When I was born I was _22_ inches long

and weighed _7_ pounds and _10_ ounces.

Today I am _____ feet and _____ inches tall

and weigh _____ pounds.

My hair is _Long and Brown and Straight_,
(What color? Curly or straight? Long or short?)

and my eyes are _Brown_.
(What color? Small, medium, or large?)

Well, I have to go now. But I will write again soon!

Love,

Paula

GLUE or TAPE a
photograph of your
BABY-SELF here.

GLUE or TAPE a
photograph of your
TODAY-SELF here.

Then & Now

TAPE a *small* lock of
your HAIR here.
(*Be careful*—or you'll
end up with a bald
spot!)

USE an ink pad or a
little bit of paint
to put your
FINGERPRINT here.
(REMEMBER—
no one has one just
like yours!)

These are a few
of my
FAVORITE

COLORS

Here are my favorite colors:

1. BlaKK
2. Pink
3. P
4. _____

5. _____
6. _____
7. _____
8. _____

Here's a rainbow of my favorite colors!

THINGS

FOODS

1. _____
2. _____
3. _____
4. _____
5. _____

TV SHOWS
(OR MOVIES OR PLAYS)

1. _____
2. _____
3. _____
4. _____
5. _____
6. _____
7. _____
8. _____
9. _____
10. _____

HOBBIES
OR ACTIVITIES

1. _____
2. _____
3. _____
4. _____
5. _____

And here–
TA-DA!

is a picture of me *doing* one of my favorite things!

_____, 19_____

Dear Diary,

    Hi! It's me again. I think it's time for me to tell you about my family now.

    My father's name is _____, and my mother's name is _____.

My father is a_____, and my mother is a_____.

    I have _____ brothers and _____ sisters.

Their names and ages are: _____

_____

_____.

    I live in a/an _____
(house? apartment? townhouse? condo?)

with _____.

Our address is _____,
house, building, or apartment number/street name

_____, _____.
city   state   zip code

And our telephone number is (_____)_____.
area code

    Are you enjoying my letters? I sure hope so!

        Love,

        _____

        Turn the page!

P.S.:

There are *other* people in my family, too!
Here are some of their names:

Stepparents

_____

_____

Grandparents

_____

_____

_____

Uncles

_____

_____

_____

Stepbrothers and sisters

_____

_____

_____

Aunts

_____

_____

_____

Cousins

_____

_____

_____

YIKES!

I almost forgot to tell you
about the ANIMALS in my family!

Here are the animals I *used* to have:

_____

_____

_____

Here are the animals I have now:

_____

_____

_____

And here are the animals I *hope* to get
in the future:

_____

_____

_____

_____

Here's a drawing (or a map) of my room:

And here's a list of my most favorite toys or games . . .

1. _____

2. _____

3. _____

4. _____

5. _____

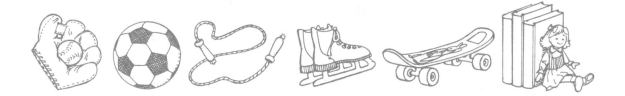

and my most favorite stories or books . . .

1. _____

2. _____

3. _____

4. _____

5. _____

_____, 19_____

Dear Diary,

    I'm back—with Letter Number Three! (This writing business isn't so hard, once you get the hang of it!)

    Anyway—now that I've told you some of the basics about my family, let's move on to S-C-H-O-O-L!

    The name of my school is _____

_____,

and our principal is _____.

    Our secretary is _____;

our nurse is _____;

and our head custodian is _____.

    I'm in grade _____, room number _____,

and my teacher is_____.

    There are _____ girls and _____ boys

in our class, and I like _____ of them.
                                (all? most? some?)

    Our music teacher is _____,

our art teacher is _____,

and our gym teacher is _____.

(Other special teachers are: _____

_____.)

    Got to go—out of room!

                   Love,

                   _____

CLASS LIST

Here are the names
of the boys in our class:

Here are the names
of the girls in our class:

CLASS RECORDS

The tallest girl in our class is _____.

The tallest boy in our class is _____.

The tallest *kid* in our class is _____.

The shortest girl in our class is _____.

The shortest boy in our class is _____.

The shortest *kid* in our class is _____.

The oldest girl in our class is _____.

The oldest boy in our class is _____.

The oldest *kid* in our class is _____.

The youngest girl in our class is _____.

The youngest boy in our class is _____.

The youngest *kid* in our class is _____.

Here are some important birthdays I want to remember.

_____

_____

_____

_____

_____

FRIENDS & ENEMIES

My *first* three best friends are:

1. _____

2. _____

3. _____

My *second* three best friends are:

1. _____

2. _____

3. _____

One time I got angry with my friend when:

_____

_____

_____

This is the way we worked things out:

_____

_____

_____

CLASS RULES

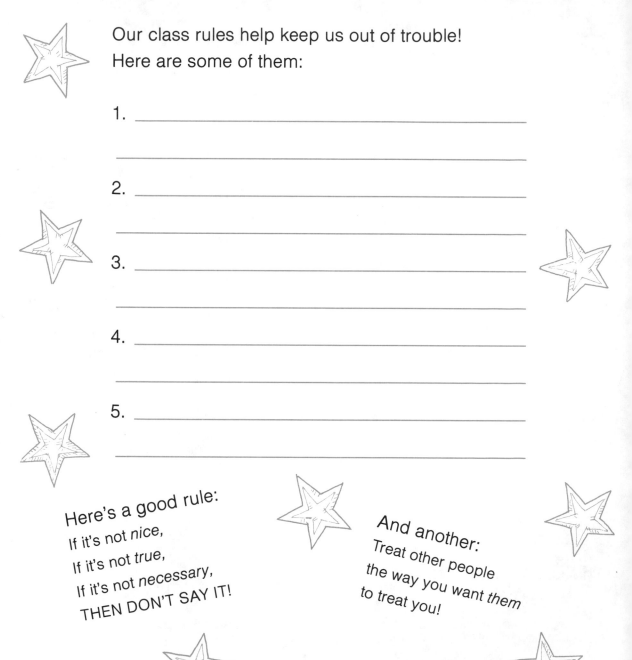

Our class rules help keep us out of trouble!
Here are some of them:

1. _____

_____

2. _____

_____

3. _____

_____

4. _____

_____

5. _____

_____

Here's a good rule:
If it's not *nice*,
If it's not *true*,
If it's not *necessary*,
THEN DON'T SAY IT!

And another:
Treat other people
the way you want *them*
to treat you!

REPORT CARDS

My BEST subjects are:

1. _____

2. _____

3. _____

4. _____

5. _____

My WORST subjects are:

1. _____

2. _____

3. _____

4. _____

5. _____

If I could afford my own, personal, private tutor
for just ONE subject,
it would be _____.

"If I had just 3 wishes . . ."

I would wish that . . .

1. _____

_____

_____

_____

2. _____

_____

_____

_____

3. _____

_____

_____

_____

Stories, stories, even DIARIES love stories!

The next page has been left *blank*
so that you can fill it
with one of your best stories ever.
Look down below for some story-starter ideas . . .

One morning I woke up and found out that I was only *five inches tall!*

If I could go *anywhere* in the whole, wide world . . .

If I could *trade places* with anyone, anywhere, I . . .

If I could change just one bad habit, it would be . . .

You'll never guess what my *earliest memory* is!

I REALLY get into a bad mood when . . .

If my allowance were one hundred dollars a week, . . .

The best thing about my age is . . .

The worst thing about my age is . . .

If I ruled the world, there'd be some CHANGES made!

_____, 19_____

Dear Diary,

CONGRATULATE ME! I MADE IT TO THE END OF
PART ONE!

Sooooooooooo—now that you know a lot of stuff about
me and my family and friends and school and
everything . . . .
I'm going to turn the page and start telling you about things
that happen each month. Don't worry if I skip a month because
I'll be talking to you again soon.

Don't do anything I wouldn't do!

Love,

_____

XOXOXO

P.S. I'm going to skip ahead to whichever
month it is when I begin this section.

PART TWO STARTS ON THE NEXT PAGE ↓

January, 19_____

Dear Diary,

    What a month this has been!

We went back to school after winter vacation, we celebrated
Martin Luther King, Jr.'s birthday, and I made some New Year's
resolutions.

    Let me tell you all about it . . . .

_____

_____

_____

_____

_____

_____

_____

_____

_____

_____

_____

_____

_____

_____

_____

_____

_____

Love,

_____

LOOKING AHEAD TO NEXT MONTH—FEBRUARY!
Groundhog Day, Lincoln's birthday, Washington's birthday,
President's Day . . . and, of course, VALENTINE'S DAY!!!

February, 19_____

Dear Diary,

What a great month THIS has been!
Let me tell you all about it!!!

_____

_____

_____

_____

_____

_____

_____

_____

_____

_____

_____

_____

_____

_____

_____

_____

_____

_____

_____

_____

Love,

_____

LOOKING AHEAD TO NEXT MONTH—MARCH!
St. Patrick's Day, windy days, kite-flying days . . .
AND THE FIRST OFFICIAL DAY OF S-P-R-I-N-G!!!!!!!!!!

March, 19_____

Dear Diary,

    A lot happened this past month—funny things and not-so-funny things.

    Some of them I want to remember, and some of them I want to forget!

    Here's what happened . . .

_____

_____

_____

_____

_____

_____

_____

_____

_____

_____

_____

_____

_____

_____

_____

_____

_____

_____

Love,

_____

LOOKING AHEAD TO NEXT MONTH—APRIL!

April Fool's Day! Changes in the weather! Maybe lots of rain!

Any birthdays? I'd better write them down, so I don't forget.

April, 19_____

Dear Diary,

Well, let me tell you—April Fool's Day this year was *something else*! Let me tell you all about it.

_____

_____

_____

_____

_____

_____

_____

_____

_____

Love,

_____

LOOKING AHEAD TO NEXT MONTH—MAY!
May Day! Mother's Day! Memorial Day! And more!

May, 19_____

Dear Diary,

    What a busy time of year this is—what with school coming to an end and everything.

    So—listen up! I've got A LOT to tell you!

_____

_____

_____

_____

_____

_____

_____

_____

_____

_____

_____

_____

_____

_____

_____

_____

_____

_____

_____

_____

_____

Love,

_____

LOOKING AHEAD TO NEXT MONTH—JUNE!
Father's Day! Last report card day!! SUMMER VACATION!!!

June, 19_____

Dear Diary,

    Well, here we are—smack in the middle of SUMMERTIME!

    Oh, those lazy, hazy, crazy days of summer!!

    Let me tell you all about them—and about some of my GOOFY friends!!!

_____

_____

_____

_____

_____

_____

_____

_____

_____

_____

Love,

_____

LOOKING AHEAD TO NEXT MONTH—JULY!
The Fourth of July (Independence Day)! Fireworks!
Picnics! Ice cream! And more!

July, 19_____

Dear Diary,

    Sit back, relax, and I will tell you about . . .
where I've been and where I want to go on my
FANTASY VACATION . . .

_____

_____

_____

_____

_____

_____

_____

_____

_____

_____

_____

_____

_____

_____

_____

_____

_____

_____

_____

_____

Love,

_____

LOOKING AHEAD TO NEXT MONTH—AUGUST!
The "dog days" of summer! The last month of summer!! HELP!!!

August, 19_____

Dear Diary,

    I can't believe it, but it's true: IT'S TIME FOR
A NEW SCHOOL YEAR!

    Let me tell you what I'm looking forward to the most—
and what I'm *dreading* the most. . . .

_____

_____

_____

_____

_____

_____

_____

_____

_____

_____

Love,

_____

LOOKING AHEAD TO NEXT MONTH—SEPTEMBER!
Labor Day! Cooler weather! And more!

September, 19_____

Dear Diary,

Well, I never thought I'd make it to the end of the first month of the new school year, but—I DID IT! I SURVIVED!

This year's class is different from last year's.

Let me explain. . . .

_____

_____

_____

_____

_____

_____

_____

_____

_____

_____

Love,

_____

LOOKING AHEAD TO NEXT MONTH—OCTOBER!
Columbus Day *AND* YOU-KNOW-WHAT DAY...
HALLOWEEN!!!!!!!!!!!!!!!!!!!!

October, 19_____

Dear Diary,

    Get ready to hear about the wildest, craziest, goofiest Halloween ever! Ready or not, here goes!!

_____

_____

_____

_____

_____

_____

_____

_____

_____

_____

Love,

_____

LOOKING AHEAD TO NEXT MONTH—NOVEMBER!
Election Day! Veterans' Day! And . . . . . THANKSGIVING!!

November, 19_____

Dear Diary,

     I'm going to pretend that I am a TURKEY—
and tell you what November was like from a *TURKEY'S*
POINT OF VIEW!!

_____

_____

_____

_____

_____

_____

_____

_____

_____

_____

_____

Love,

_____

LOOKING AHEAD TO NEXT MONTH—DECEMBER!
Chanukah! Christmas!! Winter Vacation!!!

December, 19_____

Dear Diary,

What a month DECEMBER has been!
Where shall I start?

_____

_____

_____

_____

_____

_____

_____

_____

_____

_____

_____

Love,

_____

LOOKING AHEAD TO NEXT MONTH—JANUARY!
New Year's Day! A brand-new year! Hip, hip, hooray!

_____, 19_____

Dear Diary,

     Well, here we are—on the last page.

     It's been fun talking to you.

     I'm going to save this book that I've made
and read it over a year from now. And then again *five* years
from now! And then again *ten* years from now!

       *   *   *   *   *

     And . . . . .
I think I just might start another diary
and start filling it up with *more* of my thoughts.

     So . . . . .
instead of THE END,
this is THE BEGINNING!

          Love,

_____

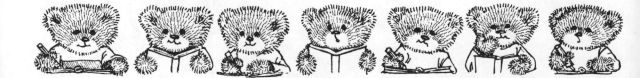